modern british bookbindings

An Exhibition of modern British bookbinding by Members of Designer Bookbinders

The Pierpont Morgan Library, New York
19 October–30 November 1971
The Newberry Library, Chicago
5 January–3 February 1972
The University Research Library
University of California, Los Angeles
1–29 March 1972
The Victoria and Albert Museum, London
14 June–16 July 1972

Designer Bookbinders London 1971

Copyright © Designer Bookbinders
12 Cornwall Mansions, 33 Kensington Court, London W8 5BG

Edited by Ivor Robinson and Bernard Middleton
Designed by Philip Smith
Set in Monotype Ehrhardt and Univers
Text printed on High White Matt Mellotex
Plates printed on Invercarron White Art
Cover Cornwall Board

SBN 9500765 1 1

Library of Congress Catalogue Card No. 76-153405

Printed in Great Britain at the University Press, Oxford

Foreword
Ivor Robinson, *President, Designer Bookbinders*

A representative exhibition of British fine bookbinding was last seen in the United States of America during the years 1961–2. Two years previously a group of books had been sent to Germany and since those dates our Society has held overseas exhibitions in the Royal Library, Stockholm, 1966, and in the Royal Library at The Hague, 1967. In 1965 it contributed to larger British Council exhibitions at Helsinki and Oslo. All of these exhibitions were held under the Society's earlier name, 'The Guild of Contemporary Bookbinders'. During 1968 the Society was reorganized and renamed 'Designer Bookbinders'.

The declared aims of Designer Bookbinders are to promote and exhibit the art of the hand-bound book and to seek to exert a progressive influence on the design and technique of bookbinding.

The Society exists mainly by virtue of its own efforts and the goodwill of patrons and friends. It receives no annual supporting grant from any governmental or industrial source.

Designer Bookbinders has three membership categories, namely 'Members'—practising bookbinders who actively support the objects of the Society and who produce, and make available, bindings for exhibition purposes; 'Associate Members'—persons interested in bookbinding and who wish to support the objects and work of the Society other than in a practising capacity; and 'Honorary Members'—persons who have rendered singular service to bookbinding or to the Society.

As the principal bookbinding society in Great Britain, Designer Bookbinders can justly claim to be the main custodian of the craft in the country today and a major assurance for its future survival and development.

Within the last twenty years there has been a remarkable growth of communication between bookbinders, not only nationally, but also and importantly at an international level. This may be ascribed to a variety of reasons. The formation in other countries of societies similar to our own has in turn encouraged group contacts. Exhibitions arranged by these national societies have allowed both public and professional appreciation of their existence and shown current trends in the craft. Craftsmen, teachers, and students of the craft have been increasingly able to visit binderies, exhibitions, and collections in other countries and also to work abroad. The establishment of Centro del Bel Libro at Ascona, Switzerland, created a necessary focal point for international bookbinding, inviting a general response including British participation. Of additional significance has been the rapid international cross-fertilization of research information following the tragic flood disaster at Florence in 1966, and in this context the biographical notes included in this catalogue indicate the important role played by Members of Designer Bookbinders in the subsequent rescue and restoration procedures.

It would be unlikely that the occurrences and activities mentioned should not considerably have affected and influenced the work of bookbinders showing in this exhibition. The quest for perfection is constant, yet the goal is elusive. The creative artist–craftsman is continually siting his objective further along the path of personal development. To him, a binding completed is a binding completed—the best is always yet to come.

The craft itself is exacting and its processes are slow. The problems of selecting, cataloguing, and dispatching an exhibition overseas are complex and lengthy. A time lag, therefore, is inevitable. In presenting this exhibition we have endeavoured to make a balanced selection from work produced during the last few years. The books we would like to have put on display are those now in our presses and on our drawing-boards. Regrettably, these must wait for another occasion.

Preface

Charles Ryskamp, *Director, The Pierpont Morgan Library, New York*

During the past seventeen years Members of Designer Bookbinders have exhibited their work annually in London and in other cities of Great Britain. The Society has also become well known in Europe and America through its own exhibitions and as a part of larger exhibitions devoted to British book production. We are as well most grateful to it for the important role it played in rescue and restoration work in Florence after the floods of 1966.

These craftsmen are part of a rich tradition of British bookbinding which goes back many centuries. One can think back as far as the twelfth century when the English made elaborately ornamented blind-tooled bindings; to the Tudor velvet bindings embroidered with metallic and silken threads; to the Stuart 'Cottage Style' bindings; to great men of the eighteenth century, most notably Roger Payne; and to T. J. Cobden-Sanderson, at the end of the nineteenth century, who has often been called 'the father of modern English bookbinding'.

More recently collectors of fine bindings have prized the work of Douglas Cockerell, a pupil and follower of Cobden-Sanderson, and Edgar Mansfield, Past President of the Society. The Members of Designer Bookbinders are largely responsible for the continuation of excellent and original craftsmanship in binding today in Great Britain.

Until recent years the patronage and collecting of fine contemporary British bindings was rapidly dying out. Owing to the work of Designer Bookbinders, the situation is now changing. A new generation of collectors of British bindings has sprung up and has stimulated outstanding craftsmanship, but there is still not the kind of patronage that the French craft-binders have known in the twentieth century. Nor have the leading English artists commonly devoted their skills to the illustrating and decorating of fine books as in France, which is no doubt one of the most important reasons for this lack of patronage.

The present exhibition of the work of Designer Bookbinders is an impressive testimony to the new vitality of British craftsmanship. Over fifty exhibits illustrating this achievement will be shown across the United States at the Pierpont Morgan Library, New York; the Newberry Library, Chicago; and the Library of the University of California, Los Angeles. After the books return from the American tour they will be shown at the Victoria and Albert Museum, London.

The suggestion for this exhibition and the conception of it are owing principally to Mr. Anthony Fair, of Sotheby & Co.; Mr. Frederick B. Adams, Jr., Director Emeritus of the Pierpont Morgan Library; Mr. Ivor Robinson, President of Designer Bookbinders; and Miss Elizabeth Greenhill, Hon. Secretary, Designer Bookbinders. They have all shown extraordinary interest in every aspect of the plans for this American tour. We are most grateful to the lenders to the exhibition; their generosity is acknowledged in the descriptions of the books and elsewhere in this catalogue.

John Harthan, *Keeper of the Library, The Victoria and Albert Museum, London*

In his 'Room and Book', a perceptive analysis of aesthetic values in design published in 1932, the late Paul Nash lamented that the decoration of English book covers showed little inventiveness of design or variety in treatment. Yet he saw no reason, except possibly economic, why leatherbound books should not be tooled with modern designs in the same idiom already found in contemporary furniture and textiles. He further discerned in the revival of patterned paper-making, begun in the early twentieth century by Lucien Pissarro at the Eragny Press, and continued in the papers designed by Lovat Fraser and others for the Curwen Press, a means both aesthetically and commercially viable whereby the external appearance of books could be given new life and brought into line with current artistic trends. Were Nash the artist to return today he would find that his *cri de coeur* did not go altogether unheeded and that times indeed have changed.

If hand bookbinding is now regarded in England as a legitimate vehicle for artistic expression, just recognition for this development is due to Sydney, son of Douglas Cockerell, and Edgar Mansfield, two leading teachers and exponents of the craft whose influence was decisive in the period immediately before, during, and after the Second World War. Their example and inspired teaching, continued by many pupils and followers, culminated in the founding of the Guild of Contemporary Bookbinders in 1955 by a group of binders anxious to break away from traditional forms of fine binding and to establish new standards of design and execution which could bear comparison with those of the other applied arts. Reconstituted in 1968 under the name of Designer Bookbinders this group now presents a selection of its Members' work which, it is hoped, besides pleasing the eye will provide valid recognition of books as works of art in their own right.

The concept of 'original' binding, in the sense of an original design made for a specific book, is largely a twentieth-century invention which has opened up new dimensions for the art of the book. In earlier periods binding design had little relation to the text within the book but reflected, usually somewhat tardily, the common ornamental styles of the period. Today the artist-binder regards the book on which he is working with considerably more respect than his predecessors. He studies the text of his author, the style and colour of the illustrations, even peculiarities of typography and layout and only then, by choice, produces a design for the covers which will be a personal synthesis reflecting the different elements of the whole book. It follows from this new attitude that binding is now regarded as a three-dimensional enterprise in which as much attention may be given to the invisible parts of a book's structure as to its external embellishment. English binders, unlike some of their French colleagues, usually undertake all the 'forwarding' processes of sewing the sheets of text, attaching the boards, working the silk headbands, covering in leather, and so on. They regard the book as an architectural unit and not simply as a flat surface awaiting decoration. Too much is sometimes made of the differences between French and English practice, of the distinction between the artist-designer, who may have no binding technique or experience, and the executant-craftsman who carries out the designs of others (one has only to think of the superlative designs of Charles Ricketts and their seminal influence), but there can be no doubt that the English binder's involvement at every stage of his work, and the necessity for surmounting an occasional limitation in one or other of his specialist techniques (about forty skilled operations are involved in the designing and binding of a book) produces work of the most diverse and plastic quality. In an age of aesthetic freedom and of extreme permissiveness in painting and the graphic arts it is worth noting that the technical demands of hand binding are so vigorous that self-discipline of this kind is a prerequisite for significant work. The most important contribution of Designer Bookbinders to the evolution of their historic craft may well be the bridging of this gap between designer and craftsman. The present exhibition shows what the designer-executant can do. It is the more to be welcomed since Great Britain has no permanent exhibition hall, comparable to the Centro del Bel Libro at Ascona, Switzerland, where fine examples of contemporary binding and of the other branches of the art of the book may be seen. But sound training, experience, artistic sensibility, and suitable books are not enough. If hand binding is to survive in the modern world, enlightened patronage must also play its part.

The catalogue of the Exhibition has been prepared by members of the Exhibition Committee. It is introduced by two essays

contributed by practising binders. Mr. Bernard Middleton
discusses specific techniques and innovations of English binding
in an historical setting while Mr. Philip Smith examines some
of the aesthetic implications when bookbinding design is treated
as an authentic medium of art. These differing but
complementary points of view serve to place the Exhibition
in a contemporary context and to establish the book as a
document of its time.

Bernard Middleton, *London*

At different times through the centuries British fine binding has reached notably high standards and particularly so during the second half of the seventeenth century and in the late eighteenth and early nineteenth centuries. In these and at other periods British bookbinders have been responsible for the introduction of interesting and important innovations in technique and design, yet in spite of this, in Great Britain the craft has never enjoyed the high status and regard accorded to it in France and Germany. For centuries the bookbinder was among the lowest paid of British skilled workers. Even today he is paid less than a great many other skilled craftsmen and, in consequence, trade firms are fast declining in quality and output.

Occasionally, and mainly in the second half of the seventeenth century and in the nineteenth century, the best British work has ranked with the best done elsewhere, but it must be admitted that this was sometimes due to the influence of certain foreign immigrants. Names such as Staggemeier, Welcher, Kalthoeber, and Hering come to mind, all of whom arrived from Germany late in the eighteenth century, whilst the Austro-Hungarian Joseph Zaehnsdorf arrived in London in the 1830s and founded one of the finest bookbinding firms in Europe.

Native British enterprise and imagination were not entirely lacking, however. Among the more interesting of our innovations may be included hidden fore-edge paintings (mid seventeenth century), painting beneath transparent vellum (c. 1785), cloth casing for edition work (c. 1823), and the blocking press (1832). The doubtful honour of having invented the unsewn (caoutchouc) binding (1836) also falls to the British.

Until the seventeenth century there was little book-cover decoration that could be described as markedly British in style and origin, but thereafter came developments which could justifiably claim this distinction. Foremost among these is the 'Cottage' style which was popular during the second half of the seventeenth century and the first half of the eighteenth. Later in the eighteenth century there were stained calf bindings in the Etruscan manner, and also the finely tooled bindings of Roger Payne, among the first to be related to the contents of the book. Little of note happened from then until the late 1880s when came a revolution rather than an innovation in British bookbinding design and outlook.

Amateurism has played an important part in many facets of the British way of life and this was the case with bookbinding at the end of the nineteenth century and later. The first to play a major role was T. J. Cobden-Sanderson, who turned to the craft at the age of forty-three after a career at the Bar. At a time when most trade designs were pastiche or derivative he introduced a new and refreshing decorative style and eschewed many harmful commercial practices.

Cobden-Sanderson's pupil at the Doves Bindery was Douglas Cockerell, another man of liberal education. He also developed his own style of designing and quickly exerted widespread influence on the quality of materials and techniques employed by amateur and, though to a lesser degree, professional bookbinders. These two original thinkers and many others who followed in their tradition were amateur only in the sense that they were not apprenticed to trade firms and subject therefore to all the technical straitjackets and design inhibitions which such training would have involved.

The advent of Cobden-Sanderson to bookbinding marked the beginning of the division of British bookbinding into two (often antagonistic) groups. On the one hand were the trade binders, many of them highly skilled but employing hackneyed designs and often thoughtlessly using techniques that were suspect both chemically and structurally; while on the other, there were the non-trade binders, most of whom had lower standards of execution but possessed the advantages of being less tightly bound by conventions tending to encourage pernicious practices such as the use of acids for leather staining, the excessive thinning of materials for ultra-fine finish, and other methods which had the additional effect of denaturizing these materials. The two groups can be seen to have been mutually complementary (though not often complimentary) in that the trade has to some extent been made aware of the desirability of using proven materials and good structural techniques, while providing the non-trade binders with examples of professional skills which they in turn could strive to emulate within the terms of their own convictions.

Between the two world wars the trade was in the ascendancy,
being given most of the important commissions, but during the
last twenty-five years non-trade binders have come to the
fore and now largely dominate British hand-bookbinding due
to the distinguished contributions of figures such as
Roger Powell (past Member of Designer Bookbinders), Sydney
Cockerell, and Peter Waters, with their concern for the structural
and chemical well-being of books; together with the achievements
of Edgar Mansfield in the field of bookbinding design.

Only recently has bookbinding emerged as a field of purely artistic expression. This development has been part of the radical change in conceptions of art during this century and the move away from 'great ideas' into regions of technical innovation, spontaneity, and the exploration of hidden aspects of the human mind. These movements cannot but have had an influence on the crafts. All the creative disciplines are pushing beyond previous limits. Craft tends towards design, design towards art, and art towards life. Bookbinding the craft has moved towards bookbinding the art and it is possibly the one discipline which could provide a bridge between 'great ideas' and the new conceptions.

There are books for all occasions, and to be relevant a book must function in a manner appropriate to the occasion. The throw-away value of the paperback book is relevant in relation to the vast turnover of ephemeral and peripheral literature. Books requiring a more extended life-span receive the somewhat superior treatment of the mass-produced hardback.

Though the Bible, Plato, and Shakespeare, as well as Mailer and Ginsberg, may be universally read in paperback, the discerning bibliophile demands a more permanent and aesthetic treatment for his books, with 'decoration' introduced into the binding. This is the province of the artist-bookbinder who now feels that an original bookbinding design is sufficient justification in itself for creative expression. The book which is intended to be treated as an art object should be designed for this purpose, not only aesthetically but structurally. Every aspect of its production should be queried—whether, for example, it requires headbands, firm boards, squares, spine lettering, even a rectangular shape—all of which are features of books in other contexts.

The codex form as an expressive object combines many dimensions which may be exploited by the artist. The body of the book may be viewed as a rectangular solid. The inter-relationship of the parts may be varied by the disposition of the boards and leaves about the hinges. The outer surfaces of the book include spine, board surfaces, and all the edges. The book is a tactile and variable solid. Its text provides two further dimensions—the duration period of reading and the dimensions of idea, thought, and emotions. The bookbinding design may attempt to integrate all these qualities into an ideograph, representative of the book as a whole.

Unlike the French bookbinding-designer, dependent upon a team of skilled technicians for the ultimate realization of his intentions, the British bookbinder must of necessity learn to exploit his many non-specialist skills. Indeed, many discoveries and aesthetic innovations can be credited to British bookbinders as a result of a working awareness and the questioning of techniques and structural requirements which, combined with a feeling for the natural properties of materials, give to our bindings a characteristic plastic quality. Some British innovations can be noted in the books shown in this exhibition—the induced graining of leather originated by Edgar Mansfield and now finding developed expression in the work of Anthony Cains and Sally Lou Smith; the monumental shapes wrapped by restless gold lines on Ivor Robinson's handsome bindings; the admirable graphic expression on the stabilized vellum bindings of Sydney Cockerell; or in my own work the feathered onlay and maril techniques (devised to allow a more fluid, colourful, and organic treatment of imagery) and most recently, the book-wall, where linked designs bring unity to a multiplicity of volumes ranged adjacent to each other.

Artistically it is no longer considered sufficient to cover the sides of books with arbitrary decorative patterns, or simply to evoke the title by mere illustrative means. The springboard for the artist-binder is the author's text which gives the book its *raison d'être*. When the significance of the text has been considered in depth and its essence embodied in an open-ended visual image capable of valid interpretation, then may the book become a total and unique work of art.

Anthony Cains
Born 1936, London, England

Biography

Commenced bookbinding through a formal apprenticeship to
the London commercial bindery of E. A. Neale. Subsequently
attended the London School of Printing and Graphic Arts (now
the London College of Printing) where he studied under various
lecturers including Edgar Mansfield, Bernard Middleton, and
Ivor Robinson. At Guildford he received further tuition from
William Matthews and later became an assistant to Sydney
Cockerell at Grantchester, Cambridge. Anthony Cains has
himself taught bookbinding at Luton School of Art, Farnham
School of Art, Camberwell School of Arts and Crafts, and the
London College of Printing. He now lives in Florence where
he is Technical Consultant to the Restoration Centre of the
Biblioteca Nazionale Centrale.

Of particular importance in recent bindings has been his
exploration into the tactile, decorative, and expressive qualities
of folded and moulded leather which, manipulated during the
covering process, provides the medium with greatly extended
plastic possibilities.

Collections

The British Museum and private collections.

Address

58 Via Desiderio da Settignano, Florence, Italy.

Bookbindings

1   Great Houses
By Nigel Nicolson. Photography by Ian Graham. Published by
Weidenfeld & Nicolson, London, 1968. Illustrated with
photographs throughout. Size 12½ × 10 in., 312 × 255 mm.
Bound in white moulded goatskin. Dark-blue morocco inlays
blind blocked with wood engravings. Leather joints with
dark-blue morocco doublures. Gilt edges. 1970. Protective
drop-back box.
Collection: The Countess of Iveagh.
Plate 1

2   Pergamon World Atlas
Printed in Poland and published by Pergamon Press, 1968.
Size 16 × 12½ in., 405 × 317 mm.
Bound in undyed goatskin with raised and moulded decoration.
Blocked in blind. Leather joints with green goatskin doublures.
Top edge gilt. Protective drop-back box.
Collection: The Lord Wardington.
Plate 2

Jeff Clements
Born 1934, Plymouth, Devonshire, England

Biography

Studied at Plymouth College of Art and at the Central School
of Arts and Crafts, London. Became lecturer in bookbinding at
Plymouth College of Art. Since 1957 has practised as a graphic
designer specializing in book design and with a personal interest
in experimental and creative typography. He has also designed
book covers for publishers' mass-production editions. In 1965 he
was appointed as Principal Lecturer in Graphic Design at
Newport College of Art, South Wales.

In his individual bookbinding Jeff Clements has made
considerable use of black morocco over sculptured boards, or
alternatively with impressed forms but in either case without
gold or colour on the exterior surfaces. More recently, however,
he has modified his designing and begun to make a selective use
of subdued yet powerful inlaid primary forms, normally
isolated from each other but strongly interactive.

Sydney M. Cockerell
Born 1906, London, England

Publications

Bookbinding, Arco Publications, London, 1963.

Collections

British Museum, Victoria and Albert Museum, and private collections in the Netherlands, Scandinavia, and the U.S.A.

Address

The Orchard, Redwick, Magor, Monmouthshire, NP6 3DE.

Bookbindings

3   Roman Imperial Coins

By Laura Breglia and translated by Peter Green. Published by Thames & Hudson, London, 1968. Size $9\frac{5}{8} \times 9\frac{1}{8}$ in., 245×350 mm.
Bound in amber morocco over sculptured boards. Inlaid with beige, grey, and brick-red and tooled in blind. Light-brown suede doublures. All edges gilt. Protective drop-back box in grey buckram.

4   The Iliad of Homer

Translated by Alexander Pope. Published by The Limited Editions Club, London, 1931, in an edition limited to 1,500 of which this is No. 1253. Typography by Jan van Krimpen printed by J. Enschedé en Zonen, Haarlem, Holland.
Size $13\frac{3}{4} \times 8\frac{1}{4}$ in., 350×210 mm.
Bound in black morocco, inlaid with amber and grey leathers with blind tooling. Olive-green suede doublures, gilt edges. Drop-back box covered in grey buckram.
Collection: Leon Drucker Esq.
Plate 3

Biography

Trained in London at the Central School of Arts and Crafts and in 1923 became a partner with his father, Douglas Cockerell, in the firm of Douglas Cockerell & Son. He has lectured at the Central School of Arts and Crafts, the Royal College of Art, and at the School of Librarianship, University College, London. Associations include Honorary Membership of the Society of Scribes and Illuminators, Fellowship of the Royal Society of Arts, Fellowship of the International Institution for Conservation of Historic and Artistic Works, Membership of the Double Crown Club, and Membership of the Art Workers' Guild (of which he was Master in 1961).

Sydney Cockerell is a specialist and an international consultant in the fields of book restoration and conservation, whilst his contribution to the revival and development of the art of marbling paper is universally acknowledged. In his bookbinding, with the co-operation of his assistants and the scribe Joan Rix Tebbut, he has made distinguished use of vellum as a covering material, the decoration of which is frequently calligraphic and heightened with gold tooling.

Publications

Marbling Paper, Russell, Hitchin, 1934.
Appendix to Douglas Cockerell's *Bookbinding and the Care of Books*, Pitman, London and New York, 1948.
The Repairing of Books, Sheppard Press, London, 1958.
Contributor to *The Calligrapher's Hand Book*, Faber, London, 1956.
Contributor to *The Encyclopaedia Britannica*, 1963.

Collections

British Museum, Victoria and Albert Museum, National Library of Scotland, Liverpool Public Library; private collections throughout the world.

Address

Riversdale, Grantchester, Cambridge.

Born 1937, Ringwood, Hampshire, England

Bookbindings

5 The Life of William Blake
Edited by Mona Wilson. Illustrations by William Blake. Printed by the Chiswick Press and published by the Nonesuch Press, London, 1927. Limited to an edition of 1,480 of which this is No. 1213. Text printed by letterpress. 24 illustrations. Size 10¾×7⅝ in., 273×195 mm.
Bound in natural vellum tooled in gold and black ink. Leather joints with marbled paper doublures. Gilt edges. In collaboration with Joan Rix Tebbut. Protective drop-back box in canvas. 1968
Collection: Anthony Fair Esq.

6 The Writings of William Blake
Edited by Geoffrey Keynes. Illustrations by William Blake. Printed by the Chiswick Press and published in 3 volumes by the Nonesuch Press, London, 1925. Limited to an edition of 1,500 of which this is No. 739. Text printed by letterpress. 28 illustrations (vol. 1), 10 illustrations (vol. 2), 20 illustrations (vol. 3). Size 10¾×7⅝ in., 273×195 mm.
Bound in natural vellum tooled in gold and black ink. Leather joints with marbled paper doublures. Gilt edges. In collaboration with Joan Rix Tebbut. Protective drop-back boxes in canvas. 1968
Collection: Anthony Fair Esq.
Plate 4

7 Comus
By John Milton. Illustrated by M. R. H. Farrar. Printed at the University Press, Oxford and published by the Nonesuch Press, London, 1937, in an edition limited to 950 of which this is copy No. 69. Printed by letterpress with 5 illustrations after the artist's linocuts. Size 15⅛×10⅛ in., 384×257 mm.
Bound in natural vellum tooled in gold, with hand-ruled black lines and hand-painted title on spine, in collaboration with Joan Rix Tebbut. Protective drop-back box in canvas. 1967.
Collection: Anthony Fair Esq.
Plate 5

Biography

Studied at Brighton College of Art, Guildford College of Art, and in London at the Central School of Arts and Crafts. Worked for a time at Petersfield as an assistant to Roger Powell and Peter Waters. Taught for ten years in England before moving to America where she set up a bookbinding teaching studio for the St. Crispin Bindery of New York. Appointed in 1967 to the Smithsonian Institute, in 1969 she became bookbinder and restorer at the Pierpont Morgan Library.

Despite her major professional commitment to restoration work, Deborah Evetts continues to produce and accept commissions for individual fine bindings of varied, often piquant, design styles.

Collections

The Royal Library at The Hague; private collections.

Address

The Pierpont Morgan Library, East Thirty-sixth Street, New York, N.Y., 10016, U.S.A.

Bookbindings

8 Friendship and Love
Essays by Landor, Emerson, Shelley, Bacon, Montaigne, and Lytton. Published by Arthur L. Humphreys, London, 1909, in an edition limited to 1,000. Text printed by letterpress. Size 6⅝×4¾ in., 163×120 mm.
Bound in purple Oasis morocco with beige, light-blue, and dark-green onlays, tooled in gold, yellow Moriki oriental endpapers. Leather joints, yellow and purple Moriki doublures, gilt head. Drop-back box in green buckram. 1970.

9 Benito Cereno
By Herman Melville. Illustrated by E. McKnight Kauffer and printed by the Curwen Press, London, 1929, in an edition limited to 1,650 of which this is No. 793. Text printed by letterpress. 9 illustrations hand-coloured through stencils. Size 12⅛×7¾ in., 308×197 mm.
Bound in navy-blue Chieftain morocco, with irregular red morocco onlay, blind tooled. Gilt edges. Drop-back box covered with green buckram. 1968

10 The House of Life

By Dante Gabriel Rossetti. Published by Arthur L. Humphreys, London, 1912, in an edition limited to 1,000. Text printed by letterpress. Size $5\frac{1}{2}\times4\frac{1}{4}$ in., 140×108 mm.
Bound in scarlet Oasis morocco with yellow native-dyed niger and dark-green onlays, tooled in gold, blind, and black. Moss-green Moriki endpapers, leather joints, gilt edges. Drop-back box covered in green buckram. 1970.
Plate 6

11 Sebastian Melmoth

By Oscar Wilde. Published by Arthur L. Humphreys, London, 1904, in an edition limited to 1,000. Text printed by letterpress. Size $6\frac{1}{2}\times4\frac{5}{8}$ in., 165×118 mm.
Bound in natural coloured Oasis morocco with purple, black, and green onlays, gold and blind tooling with some recessed areas, purple Moriki endpapers, leather joints, purple and lavender Moriki doublures, foredge and tail uncut, head gilt. Drop-back box covered in green linen. 1970.
Plate 7

Elizabeth Greenhill

Born 1907, Paris, France

Biography

Studied at L'École des Arts Decoratifs, Paris, and later in London at the Central School of Arts and Crafts. For many years specialized in the repair and restoration of old books and manuscripts but is now mainly engaged in individual fine bookbinding. During the winter of 1967 she worked on flood-damaged books with a group of British bookbinders at the Biblioteca Nazionale Centrale, Florence.

Honorary Secretary of Designer Bookbinders, Elizabeth Greenhill is the binder of the Gloucester Civic Bible and the Nurses Roll of Honour in Westminster Abbey.

Collections

British Museum, Victoria and Albert Museum, the Royal Library at The Hague, Sheffield University Library, Liverpool Public Library; private collections in Great Britain and abroad.

Address

12 Cornwall Mansions, 33 Kensington Court, London, W8 5BG.

Bookbindings

12 Printing with the Hand Press

By Lewis M. Allen. Illustrated by Victor A. Seward. Printed and published by the Allen Press, Kentfield, California, 1969. Limited to an edition of 140, hand-printed by letterpress. Size $11\frac{3}{4}\times8\frac{1}{2}$ in., 299×216 mm.
Bound in blue levant morocco with black leather onlays, joints, and doublures. Tooling in gold and blind. Gilt top edge. Drop-back box in black Oasis and cloth. 1970.

13 Fables of Esope

Translated by William Caxton and illustrated by Agnes Miller Parker. Printed and published by the Gregynog Press, Newtown, Montgomeryshire, 1931. Limited to an edition of 250 of which this is No. 194. Size $12\frac{1}{4}\times9$ in., 311×229 mm.
Bound in brown morocco with multicoloured onlays and brown Oasis doublures. Gold tooling and lettering on spine. Gilt top edge. Drop-back box in brown Oasis and cloth. 1970.
Collection: Anthony Fair Esq.
Plate 8

14 The Dialogue of the Dogs

By Miguel de Cervantes Saavedra. Ornament engraved by M. Dean. Printed and published by the Allen Press, Kentfield, California, 1969. Hand-printed by letterpress with hand-blocked illustrations. Size $11\frac{7}{8}\times9$ in., 302×228 mm.
Bound in light olive-green Oasis with orange and leaf-green onlays and leather joints. Grey Oasis doublures. Gold tooling and lettering on spine. Gilt top edge. Drop-back box in light-green Oasis and grey cloth. 1970.

15   Birds & Mammals of South America
By Helmut Sick. Illustrated by Axel Amuchastegui. Published
by the Tryon Gallery in association with George Rainbird,
London, 1967. Text filmset with 24 illustrations, the frontispiece
lithographed by the artist. Size 12×9 in., 305×229 mm.
Bound in brown morocco with multicoloured onlays and gold
tooling. Brown morocco joints and Ingres endpapers, gilt edges.
Drop-back box in brown morocco and cloth. Bound in 1969.
Collection: Mrs. P. L. Bradfer-Lawrence.
Plate 9

Arthur Johnson

Born 1920, London, England

Biography

Studied in London, first at Hornsey College of Art and later at
the Camberwell School of Arts and Crafts. Following the awards
of a National Diploma in Design and an Art Teaching Diploma
he himself became a lecturer in bookbinding at Hornsey College
of Art, and also at colleges in Hammersmith and Willesden.
At the present time he is appointed to the London College of
Printing.

A founder member and first Honorary Secretary of the Guild of
Contemporary Bookbinders, Arthur Johnson is a vigorous designer
and colourist whose work often exhibits a strongly primeval,
almost hieratic quality that is particularly his own.

Collections

British Museum, the Liverpool Public Library; major private
collections in Great Britain and the U.S.A.

Address

89 Clifford Road, New Barnet, Hertfordshire.

Bookbindings

16   The Horse's Mouth
By Joyce Cary, edited by Andrew Wright. Illustrated by
Joyce Cary and published by George Rainbird, London, 1957.
Text printed by letterpress with 8 lithographs. Book signed by
the editor. Size 9⅞×6⅞ in., 250×175 mm.
Bound in pink morocco with design onlaid in natural, purple, red,
blue, black, and white morocco. Tooled in blind. Title lettering
onlaid in black leather. Plain trimmed edges. Protective drop-back
box in buckram. 1970.

17   Albert Houthuesen
Introduction by Sir John Rothenstein. Printed by the Curwen
Press and published by Mercury Graphics, London, 1970, in an
edition limited to 450. Text printed by letterpress and illustrated
with 22 half-tone plates and 25 black-and-white illustrations.
Size 14½×9⅞ in., 373×250 mm.
Bound in red morocco with onlays of white, pink, and crimson,
leather set in recessed boards. Ingres endpapers. Gilt edges.
Title in gold on spine. Drop-back box covered in buckram. 1970.

18   Extinct Birds
By the Hon. Walter Rothschild. Published by Hutchinson & Co.,
London, 1907, in an edition limited to 300. Text printed by
letterpress with 42 colour half-tone plates. Size 15⅛×11⅞ in.,
385×303 mm.
Bound with green levant morocco spine and sides in Spanish
marbled sheepskin. Design onlaid in pink, white, dark blue,
light blue, crimson red, yellow, and natural coloured leathers.
Tooled in gold and blind. Leather joints and Ingres endpapers.
Top edge gilt. Drop-back box covered in buckram. 1970.
Plate 10

Trevor Jones
Born 1931, Wembley, London, England

Biography

Studied at Harrow School of Art, Middlesex. Subsequently
studied bookbinding under the direction of Arthur Johnson at
Hornsey College of Art. Holder of the National Diploma in
Design and the Art Teaching Certificate. Appointed Lecturer in
Art and Craft at St. John's College, York, on the retirement of
Laurence Town, he is now Head of the Art and Craft
Department and concerned with the training of teachers.

His bookbindings frequently employ sculptured or modelled
techniques and exploit grain tendencies for expressive purposes.
Designer of the Lectern Bible in the Chapel of Unity, Coventry
Cathedral, Trevor Jones is also a book illustrator and has an
additional interest in typography and in the graphic arts generally.

Collections

Victoria and Albert Museum; major private collections.

Address

17 Hall Rise, Haxby, York, YO3 8LP.

Bookbinding

19   Malleus Maleficarum
Translated by the Revd. Montague Summers. Published by
John Rodker, 1928, in an edition limited to 1,275 of which this is
No. 1142. Printed by letterpress. Size $11\frac{3}{4} \times 6\frac{7}{8}$ in., 299×170 mm.
Bound in white goatskin with inlays in red, ochre, and navy-blue
leather. Onlaid in red, grey, and navy-blue leather with tooling
in red, blind, and gold. Additional decoration formed by raised
and modelled leather and a recessed inlay on the front board.
Endpapers marbled by the binder on Ingres paper. Leather
joints. Titled in gold on spine. Protective chemise and slip-case.
1960.
Plate 11

Edgar Mansfield
Born 1907, London, England

Biography

Received his initial art training in New Zealand, to which
country his family had emigrated in 1912. Taught art for five
years in Dunedin before returning to London in 1934. Studied
bookbinding at the Central School of Arts and Crafts under
William Matthews and design at the Reimann School under
Elsa Taterka. After the war he was appointed to the London
College of Printing as a lecturer in design, colour, and
bookbinding design. One-man exhibitions of his work have been
held in London and abroad. A member of Meister der
Einbandkunst and a Fellow of the Royal Society of Arts, he was
from 1955 until 1968 President of the Guild of Contemporary
Bookbinders. Following his retirement from teaching in 1964
his time has been divided between London and New Zealand.

Through his cover designs, Edgar Mansfield has sought to give
visual expression to the content of the literary work by a variety
of technical means, tactile qualities, colour, and the use of
powerfully conceived inner and outer forms together with a
positive involvement of space. Known also as a sculptor, Edgar
Mansfield brought to bookbinding the attitudes of a creative
artist and his influence on the craft has been major and
profound.

Publications

Modern Design in Bookbinding—The Work of Edgar Mansfield,
Peter Owen, London; and Boston Books, Boston, 1966.

Collections

British Museum, Victoria and Albert Museum, Swedish Royal
Library, Royal Library at The Hague, Auckland Museum,
Klingspor Museum, Spencer Collection at New York Public
Library, Liverpool Public Library; private collections throughout
the world.

Addresses

18 Dartmouth Hill, London, S.E.10, and 313 Kennedy Road,
Napier, New Zealand.

Bookbindings

20   The Eclogues of Vergil
Illustrated by Maillol. Printed in English by Emery Walker Ltd.
and published by Cranach Press, 1927. Limited to an edition
of 225 of which this is No. 67. Size 13½ × 10¼ in., 343 × 260 mm.
Bound in yellow native-dyed morocco with multicoloured inlays.
Ingres endpapers. Top edge gilt.
Collection: Colin Franklin Esq.
Plate 12

21   Behold this Dreamer
By Walter de la Mare. Illustrated by Barnett Freedman.
Published by Faber & Faber, London, 1939. Text printed by
letterpress with frontispiece. Size 9⅛ × 6⅛ in., 232 × 155 mm.
Bound in blue-purple morocco. Inlaid with grey and mauve
leather and tooled in blind. Ingres endpapers. Top edge gilt.
Collection: Anthony Fair Esq.
Plate 13

22   Carmen
Sur le Texte de Prosper Mérimée. Illustrated by Picasso.
Printed by La Bibliotheque Française in Paris. Limited to an
edition of 289 of which this is No. 195. Illustrated by 38 original
etchings. Signed by Picasso. Size 13½ × 7¾ in., 343 × 192 mm.
Bound in red native-dyed morocco. Inlaid with black and ochre
leather and tooled in gold. Ingres endpapers. Head cut.

23   Le Chant des Morts
Edited by Pierre Reverdy. Illustrated by Picasso. Printed by
Teriade, Paris, 1948. Limited to an edition of 250 of which this is
No. 215. Text printed by lithography with illustrations and
decorations by lithography on every page. Signed by Picasso
and Reverdy. Size 17 × 13½ in., 432 × 343 mm.
Bound in red and black morocco. Inlaid with natural, red and
black morocco. Leather joints with Ingres endpapers. Edges
uncut. Protective drop-back box in canvas.
Collection: Anthony Fair Esq.
Plate 14

24   The Canticle of Rose—Selected Poems
By Edith Sitwell. Published by Macmillan & Co. Ltd., London,
1949. Text printed by letterpress. Size 8⅞ × 5⅞ in., 226 × 150 mm.
Bound in yellow morocco. Inlaid with red and black leather.
Tooled in blind. Cream Ingres endpapers. Top edge gilt.
Collection: Mrs. Maggy Magerstadt Rosner.
Plate 15

Bernard Middleton

Born 1924, London, England

Biography

The son of a bookbinder. Studied at the Central School of
Arts and Crafts and the London College of Printing. Served an
apprenticeship at the bindery of the British Museum. During
the war he served in the Royal Navy and afterwards became a
Craftsman-Demonstrator assistant to Roger Powell at the Royal
College of Art. Before establishing his own bindery in 1953,
he was for a time Manager of the London Bindery of Zaehnsdorf
Ltd. A Silver Medallist of the City and Guilds of London
Institute, he was for seven years Chief Examiner in General
Bookbinding for that body. His Associations include Fellowship
of the Society of Antiquaries and Fellowship of the Royal
Society of Arts.

Bernard Middleton is primarily a book restorer and an authority
in that field. Following the flooding of the Biblioteca
Nazionale Centrale in 1966 he was engaged for a time in
Florence, working on books from the damaged library.
Considering himself craftsman rather than designer, his

Ivor Robinson
Born 1924, Bournemouth, Hampshire, England

individual fine bookbindings do, nevertheless, through a traditional simplicity of means, display classic and timeless elegance.

Publications

A History of English Craft Bookbinding Technique, Hafner Publishing Company, London and New York, 1963.

Collections

British Museum, Victoria and Albert Museum, the Royal Library at The Hague; major private collections.

Address

3 Gauden Road, Clapham, London, S.W. 4.

Bookbindings

25   A History of Book Illustration
By David Bland. Printed by John Dickins & Co. and published by Faber & Faber, London, 1969. Text printed by letterpress. 404 illustrations printed by half-tone and line-blocks.
Size $10\frac{3}{4} \times 7\frac{1}{2}$ in., 273×190 mm.
Bound in black morocco over vertical raised ribs with red morocco onlays tooled in gold and blind. Gilt edges. Protective drop-back box in morocco and cloth. 1970.
Plate 16

26   European Architecture in Colour
By R. Furneaux Jordan. Published by Thames & Hudson, London, 1961. Text printed by letterpress. 112 plates printed in colour. Size $11\frac{1}{8} \times 9$ in., 283×229 mm.
Bound in light-brown Oasis morocco with gold and blind tooling. Black leather joints with black morocco flyleaves and doublures tooled in blind. Gilt edges. $\frac{1}{4}$-leather chemise and leather-edged slip-case. 1962.

27   Gems
By Mab Wilson. Printed by Mondadori, Verona, and published in London, 1967. Text printed by letterpress. About 80 monochrome and coloured plates. Size $9\frac{1}{2} \times 7\frac{5}{8}$ in., 241×194 mm.
Bound in violet Oasis morocco with gold tooling. Gilt edges. Protective drop-back box in morocco and cloth. 1970.
Plate 17

Biography

Served a formal apprenticeship in a miscellaneous bindery and also studied at Bournemouth College of Art under the direction of Eric Burdett. Awarded the Silver Medal of the City and Guilds of London Institute in 1941. After war service with the Royal Navy he worked for seven years in restoration and fine bookbinding with Harry Bailey at Salisbury and at the same time became visiting lecturer in bookbinding at Salisbury College of Art. Leaving Salisbury in 1953 he took up whole-time lecturing appointments, first at the London College of Printing and, since 1958, at Oxford Polytechnic. He has held one-man exhibitions of his work at Hantverket Gallery, Stockholm, 1963, and at Galleria del Bel Libro, Ascona, Switzerland, 1969. He was awarded Silver and Bronze Medals in the 1971 Prix Paul Bonet. In 1968 he was elected President of Designer Bookbinders. He is a member of Meister der Einbandkunst, a Fellow of the Royal Society of Arts, and a Council Member of the Federation of British Craft Societies.

In earlier bindings Ivor Robinson used multicoloured hard-edge inlays almost exclusively. More recently this discipline has given way to tooled designs in which a strictly limited number of units define irregular linear forms across covers which are frequently black, whilst any inlays act now as emphasis points, rather like seals on documents.

Publications

Introducing Bookbinding, Batsford, London, and Watson-Guptill, New York, 1968.

Collections

British Museum, Victoria and Albert Museum, Swedish Royal Library, Danish Royal Library, Gothenburg Röhsska Museum; private collections in Great Britain and abroad.

Address

67 Upper Road, Kennington, Oxford, OX1 5LN.

Bookbindings

28   The Trinity College Apocalypse
Printed by Louis Van Leer & Co. Ltd., Holland, and published by the Eugrammia Press, London and Trinity College,

Cambridge, 1967, in an edition limited to 600 of which this is No. 215. A facsimile copy of the original manuscript. Size $17\frac{1}{8} \times 11\frac{7}{8}$ in., 435×300 mm.
Bound in red morocco with gold tooling, fawn endpapers, red morocco joints, red suede doublures, grey suede flyleaves, rough gilt edges. 1968.
Collection: Anthony Fair Esq.

29   Jerusalem
By William Blake. Illustrated by William Blake and published by the Trianon Press, 1951, in an edition limited to 500 of which this is No. 286. Facsimile reproduced by collotype and hand coloured. Size $13\frac{3}{8} \times 10\frac{1}{4}$ in., 340×260 mm.
Bound in black morocco, gold tooling, black Ingres endpapers, terracotta calf doublures and flyleaves, rough gilt edges, lettered on spine. Drop-back box covered in cloth. 1967.
Collection: Anthony Fair Esq.
Plate 18

30   Samuel Palmer's Sketch-Book, 1824
By Martin Butun. Printed by Hourdebaight & Crampe, France, and Spottiswoode & Ballantyne, England. Published by the Trianon Press, 1962, in an edition limited to 586 of which this is No. 414. Text printed by letterpress with 185 collotype pages. A facsimile copy of Samuel Palmer's Sketch-Book. Size $4\frac{7}{8} \times 6\frac{5}{8}$ in., 123×167 mm.
Bound in natural Oasis, blind and gold tooling. Endpapers in brown Japanese paper with brown calf joints. 1969.
Collection: Anthony Fair Esq.

31   The Rime of the Ancient Mariner
By Samuel Taylor Coleridge. Single copy only, hand written by Pat Russell, 1968, in black and terracotta calligraphy. Size $17 \times 6\frac{1}{2}$ in., 430×165 mm.
Bound in dark-green Cape goatskin with white calf onlays, gold tooling, green Ingres endpapers, dark-green Oasis doublures, terracotta suede flyleaves. Drop-back box in black cloth. 1970.
Collection: Anthony Fair Esq.

32   The Four Gospels of the Lord Jesus Christ
Illustrated and decorated by Eric Gill. Printed and published by Robert and Moira Gibbings at The Golden Cockerel Press, 1931, in an edition limited to 500. Text printed by letterpress, with wood-engravings. Size $13\frac{1}{4} \times 9$ in., 335×230 mm.
Bound in black morocco, black Oasis inlays, black and white calf onlays, tooled in palladium, black Ingres endpapers, black Oasis joints, purple suede doublures and flyleaves, rough palladium edges. 1968.
Collection: Anthony Fair Esq.
Plate 19

33   The Wreck of the Deutschland
By Gerard Manley Hopkins. Single copy only, hand-written by Pat Russell, 1969. Size $7\frac{1}{4} \times 16$ in., 185×405 mm.
Bound in black Oasis with blue, black, grey, and purple Oasis onlays, gold tooling, black Ingres endpapers, grey suede doublures and flyleaves, gilt edges. 1969.
Collection: Anthony Fair Esq.

34   Seven Pillars of Wisdom
By T. E. Lawrence. Printed by the Alden Press and published by Jonathan Cape, London, 1935. Text printed by letterpress. Size $10\frac{1}{8} \times 7\frac{3}{8}$ in., 255×190 mm.
Bound in black Oasis, one brown onlay on front board, tooled in gold, black Ingres endpapers, black Oasis doublures, brown calf flyleaves, rough gilt edges, lettered on spine. Drop-back box in black cloth. 1970
Collection: Lt.-Col. P. L. Bradfer-Lawrence.
Plate 20

35   King Lear
By William Shakespeare. Illustrated by Oscar Kokoschka. Printed by Ganymed, Berlin, and published by Marlborough Fine Art, London, 1963, in an edition limited to 275 of which this is No. 121. Text printed by letterpress. Signed by the artist. Size $18\frac{3}{8} \times 14$ in., 465×355 mm.
Bound in brown and black morocco, tooled in blind and gold, black suede doublures, brown suede flyleaves, rough-gilt edges.

Built up letters on spine tooled in gold. Cloth covered book-box. 1967.
Collection: Anthony Fair Esq.
Plate 21

36   Le Georgiche di Virgilio
Illustrated by Giacomo Manzù. Printed by Giovanni Mardersteig and published by Ulrico Hoepli, Milan, 1948, in an edition limited to 165 of which this is No. 70. Text printed by letterpress with 20 etchings. Signed by the artist. Size $15\frac{1}{4}\times10\frac{7}{8}$ in., 387×277 mm.
Bound in brown morocco with natural Oasis inlay, gold tooling, green Ingres endpapers, brown morocco joints, green suede doublures and flyleaves, rough gilt edges. 1968.
Collection: Anthony Fair Esq.

Faith Shannon
Born 1938, Dehra Dun, India

Biography

Spent her childhood in India, returning to Great Britain in 1946. Studied painting and bookbinding at Belfast College of Art. Moved to London and studied bookbinding with George Frewin and William Matthews at the Central School of Arts and Crafts, and design with Edgar Mansfield at London College of Printing. Read Education at London University, Goldsmiths' College, from 1959 until 1960. Studied bookbinding and graphic design at the Royal College of Art from 1960 to 1963, the former subject under Peter Waters. Awarded the Henry Higgins Travelling Scholarship whilst at Belfast in 1958 and utilized this in 1962 touring important libraries and binderies in the U.S.A. Spent

part of 1967 in Florence working on flood-damaged books. Is married to Art Director Patrick Tofts and currently undertakes free-lance design and bookbinding commissions, together with some art teaching.

Because she considers every book to be an entirely different problem of purpose and structure, and therefore materials and appearance, Faith Shannon eschews the development of a personal style in her work, hoping thus that if any of her bindings were set side by side, they would not be recognized as being the work of one person.

Collections

The British Museum and private collections in Great Britain and abroad.

Address

18 Kings Road, Kingston-upon-Thames, Surrey.

Bookbinding

37   Something about Myself
By Siegfried Sassoon when he was eleven years of age. ('From the manuscript "More Poems" by S. L. Sassoon, with illustrations. For Mamsy from Siegfried, October 20th,–December 25th 1897'. Homage on his 80th birthday to Siegfried Sassoon). Illustrated by Margaret Adams with calligraphy reproduced by line block at the Stanbrook Abbey Press, Worcester, in an edition limited to 220 of which this is one of a few copies specially initialled by Siegfried Sassoon for Henry Sotheran Ltd., London, 1966. Size $10\frac{1}{8}\times7\frac{1}{4}$ in., 258×184 mm.
Bound in dark-brown velvet with inset silhouette miniature on vellum, glass-covered, with black silk and gold-thread-embroidered border. Velvet and linen joints, brown Japanese paper doublures. Deckle edges. Drop-back box in brown morocco, velvet, and Japanese paper.
Collection: Henry Sotheran Ltd., London.
Plate 22

Born 1928, Southport, Lancashire, England

Biography

Educated at Ackworth School, Yorkshire. Served in the Royal Air Force for three years. Studied at Southport School of Art and was introduced to bookbinding by Raymond Geering. Studied bookbinding under Roger Powell at the Royal College of Art, together with graphical subjects, and graduated with a First Class Diploma. Taught at Malvern School of Art from 1955 until 1957 when he became assistant to Sydney Cockerell. Lectured at Maidstone and Farnham Colleges of Art and in 1961 was appointed Director of Studies, Graphic Design, Waltham Forest School of Art. During 1966 and 1967 joined the British Museum team working in Florence on flood-damaged books. Is a member of the Society of Industrial Artists and Designers and of Meister der Einbandkunst. Winner of the Open Prize in the 1957 Thomas Harrison Memorial Competition and a painter exhibitor in the 1967 John Moores Liverpool Exhibition, he has held one-man exhibitions of his work at the Hampstead Civic Centre, 1964, and in 1970 at Galleria del Bel Libro, Ascona, Switzerland, and Goldsmiths' Hall, London.

Philip Smith is probably the most important colourist working anywhere in bookbinding today. His innovations of feathered, reconstituted, and sectioned (maril) leather techniques have greatly extended the field of onlay possibilities, whilst his 'book-wall' sets with their macro and micro concepts make an entirely new presentation of 'the book as an art object' theme.

Publications

The Lord of the Rings and other Bookbindings of Philip Smith, published by the author, 1970.

Collections

British Museum; Victoria and Albert Museum; Hornby Library, Liverpool; The Spencer Collection, New York Public Library; Museo del Oro, Bogota, Colombia; private collections in Great Britain, Canada, and the U.S.A.

Address

83 Nutfield Road, South Merstham, Redhill, Surrey.

Bookbindings

38   The Comanche Indians

By Lieutenant James W. Abert and edited by John Galvin. Illustrated by J. W. Abert and printed by Lawton and Alfred Kennedy. Published by John Howell of San Francisco, 1970, in an edition limited to 5,000 copies. Printed by letterpress with 26 colour half-tone illustrations and 2 fold-out maps. Size $13\frac{3}{4} \times 10\frac{1}{4}$ in., 345×260 mm.
Bound in bright-orange Cape morocco, black and tan Oasis with feathered onlays and maril in tan, ochre, blue, purple, olive, yellow, and red. Black leather joints with doublures in brown Japanese paper. Gilt edges and silk headbands. Titled in gold on a black onlay. Double box felt-lined and cloth-covered. 1970–1.
Collection: Sir John Galvin.
(This binding was specially commissioned for the American Exhibitions.)
Plate 23

39   Western America in 1846–47

By Lieutenant James W. Abert and edited by John Galvin. Illustrated by J. W. Abert and printed by Lawton and Alfred Kennedy. Published by John Howell, 1970, in an edition limited to 3,000 copies. Text printed by letterpress with 15 half-tone illustrations and 2 fold-out maps. Size $13\frac{3}{4} \times 10\frac{1}{4}$ in., 345×260 mm.
Bound in bright-orange Cape morocco, black and ochre Oasis with multicoloured feathered onlays and maril. Black leather joints with doublures in brown Japanese paper. Gilt edges and silk headbands. Titled in gold on black onlay. Double box felt-lined and cloth-covered. 1970–1.
Collection: Sir John Galvin.
(This binding was specially commissioned for the American Exhibitions.)

40   Jane Eyre

By Charlotte Brontë (Currer Bell). Illustrated by Ethel Gabin and printed by Leon Pichon of Paris. Published by Vincent Brooks Day & Son, 1923, in an edition limited to 495 of which this is copy No. 20. Text printed by letterpress with 17 original

lithographs. Size 15×11½ in., 375×290 mm.
Bound in black, grey, purple, and light-olive moroccos with feathered leather onlays and maril in black, white, grey, tan, purple, and mauve. Boards made up in low-relief letter-forms. Gilt edges and coloured silk headbands. Leather joints with brown Japanese paper doublures. Titled in geometric black leather onlay. The imagery is constructed so that by turning the binding either way horizontally different mood-landscapes may be discerned (ref. Rorschach). 1970–1.
Collection: Anthony Fair Esq.
Plate 24

41　King Lear

By William Shakespeare. Illustrated by Oscar Kokoschka and printed at the University Press, Oxford. Published by Ganymed Press Original Editions Limited, 1963, in an edition limited to 279 of which this is No. 126. Text printed by letterpress with 16 original lithographs, signed by the artist. Size 18×14¼ in., 457×360 mm.
Spine covered in purple Oasis with title blocked in black over coloured onlays. Boards attached by tongue and slot method, covered in orange Cape morocco. Image built from feathered onlays to grey morocco and inset into shallow letter-form impressions. Leather joints with purple suede doublures. Book-box covered in tan Sudanese cowhide with plastic letter-form templates incorporated under purple morocco-covered lid, tooled in blind. 1967–8.
Collection: Anthony Fair Esq.
Plate 25

42　The Lord of the Rings

By J. R. R. Tolkien. Illustrated by the author with several diagrams, charts, and 2 fold-out maps. Published by George Allen & Unwin in 1 volume on India paper. Printed by letterpress, title-page in red and black. Size 9⅛×5⅞ in., 270×150 mm. Six books assembled as a book-wall in a walnut and acrylic case made by Desmond Ryan. Size 22⅝×21⅝ in., 575×549 mm. The linked designs may be viewed from both sides.
The books are bound in various moroccos and silver kid, mainly black and grey with feathered onlays and maril in greys, silver kid, white, pink, and purple. The silver book has folds induced

in the leather. Black leather joints and doublures on photographic paper with various scrambled variations of the title. Book edges in palladium and gold. Coloured silk headbands. Titles in various positions on the spines in gold and palladium, some mixed.
This exhibit shows six linked versions of the same title to demonstrate the validity of the book-wall concept for sets of volumes. 1970–1.
Plate 26

43　Leonardo da Vinci

Published by Leisure Arts, London, 1964, under copyright of the Instituto Geografico de Agostini, Novara, Italy, in 2 volumes. Text and illustrations printed by gravure. Several colour plates. Size 14½×10½ in., 370×260 mm.
Bound with vellum spines. The black morocco-covered boards are attached by the tongue and slot method, with multicoloured maril onlays having feathered onlay edging progressing through the colour spectrum from stage to stage. Black and purple leather joints with oatmeal coloured hand-made paper doublures and endpapers. Title and volume number stencilled on spine in coloured printing inks. Double book-box with vellum spine and flaps and blind-stamped leather-covered lid. 1969.

44　Irish Fairy Tales

Edited and with Introduction by W. B. Yeats. Illustrated by Jack Yeats. Published by T. Fisher Unwin, London, 1892. Text printed by letterpress with 2 line-block engravings. Size 6⅜×4 in., 160×100 mm.
Bound in green and purple Oasis with multicoloured feathered onlays and maril. Green leather joints with hand-made paper flyleaves and doublures. Gilt edges and coloured silk headbands. Cloth-covered and felt-lined box with press-stud fasteners.
Collection: Sir John Galvin. 1969.
Plate 27

Sally Lou Smith
Born 1925, Fulton, New York, U.S.A.

Biography

Read for a B.A. degree in Economics at Wellesley College, Wellesley, Massachusetts. Since 1949 she has lived in Europe, firstly in Paris and then from 1958 in London. Studied bookbinding under the direction of John Corderoy at the Camberwell School of Arts and Crafts and set up her own bindery in 1963. Was appointed a visiting lecturer in bookbinding at Southampton College of Art for the years 1963 and 1964, at Brighton College of Art from 1963, and at the Stanhope Institute, London, from 1967. Awarded prizes in the Thomas Harrison Memorial Competition in 1961, 1962, and 1963, and First Prize in the Major J. R. Abbey Bookbinding Competition of 1965. Joined the British Museum team working in Florence on flood-damaged books from the Biblioteca Nazionale Centrale during 1966, 1967, and 1968.

The work of Sally Lou Smith evolves from the discovery of a visual image suggested initially by the literary work and subsequently influenced by graphical and technical considerations. The image is developed into a viable pattern or motif to produce bindings involving cover contrasts of colour, texture, and tooling, together with doublure treatment of great distinction.

Collections

British Museum; Victoria and Albert Museum; The Spencer Collection, New York Public Library; private collections.

Address

42a Camden High Street, London, NW1 0JH.

Bookbindings

45   The Prologue

By Geoffrey Chaucer. Illustrated by Ronald King. Published by Editions Alecto in Guildford, 1967. Limited to an edition of 125. Artist's proof copy. Text printed by letterpress.
15 illustrations printed by silk screen. Signed by the artist.
Size $21\frac{1}{4} \times 15$ in., 540×380 mm.
Bound in black levant morocco and tooled in gold. Leather joints with blue calf doublures tooled in gold. Japanese endpapers. Edges uncut. Protective box in black morocco and cloth. 1970.
Collection: Tony Appleton Esq.

46   Portraits of Wild Flowers

By Elsa Felsko. Illustrated with water-colours taken from 'Blumenatlas'. Printed by William Clowes & Sons Ltd. and published by Bruno Cassirer at Oxford in 1959. 140 illustrations printed in colour. Size $9\frac{5}{8} \times 6\frac{3}{8}$ in., 245×160 mm.
Bound in dark-blue Oasis morocco. Onlaid with green, blue, purple, and yellow ochre morocco and tooled in gold. Endpapers of Japanese paper with morocco onlays and gold tooling.
Rough-gilt edges.
Protective drop-back box with morocco spine and cloth sides.
Collection: The Countess of Iveagh.

47   A Book of Wild Flowers

By Elsa Felsko. Illustrated with water-colours taken from 'Blumenatlas'. Printed by William Clowes & Sons Ltd. and published by Bruno Cassirer at Oxford in 1963. 160 illustrations printed in colour. Size $9\frac{5}{8} \times 6\frac{3}{8}$ in., 245×160 mm. Bound in purple morocco. Onlaid with red, orange, green, and mauve morocco and tooled in gold. Japanese endpapers with morocco onlays and gold tooling. Rough-gilt edges.
Collection: The Countess of Iveagh.

48   The Iliad of Homer

Translated by Richmond Lattimore. Illustrated by Leonard Baskin. Published by the University of Chicago Press in 1962.
49 illustrations. Size $11\frac{1}{8} \times 7\frac{5}{8}$ in., 285×195 mm.
Bound in brown Oasis morocco with raised black morocco onlays and tooled in gold. Leather joints and black Oasis doublures with gold and blind tooling. Brown Ingres endpapers. Gilt edges. Protective drop-back box in black morocco and cloth. 1969.
Collection: Anthony Fair Esq.
Plate 28

49   Seven Pillars of Wisdom

By T. E. Lawrence. Published by Jonathan Cape, London, 1935. Text printed by letterpress. 54 illustrations printed by photogravure. Size $10 \times 7\frac{3}{4}$ in., 250×198 mm.
Bound in black levant morocco with crumpled tan morocco onlays and gold tooling. Leather joints and tan morocco doublures with onlays and gold tooling. Japanese endpapers.

Desmond Yardley

Born 1905, Dublin, Ireland

Rough-gilt edges. Protective drop-back box in black morocco and cloth. 1970.
Collection: Lt.-Col. P. L. Bradfer-Lawrence.
Plate 29

50   Chimes
By Dante Gabriel Rossetti. Illustrated by Birgit Skiold. Printed by Derek Redfern and published by Circle Press Publications at Guildford in 1969. Limited to an edition of 75 of which this is No. 40. Text printed by letterpress. Illustrated by 7 etchings in relief. Signed by the artist. Size $15\frac{3}{4} \times 12$ in., 400×305 mm.
Bound in blue-grey levant morocco. Onlaid with crumpled orange Oasis and full thickness red calf and tooled in gold. Leather joints with red calf doublures onlaid and tooled in gold. Japanese endpapers. Deckle edges. Protective drop-back box in blue-grey morocco and cloth. 1970.

51   Song of Solomon
Illustrated by Ronald King. Published by Circle Press Publications at Guildford in 1968. Limited to an edition of 150 of which this is No. 106. Text printed by letterpress. 15 illustrations printed by silk screen. Signed by the artist. Size $15 \times 12\frac{1}{4}$ in., 383×312 mm.
Bound in purple Oasis morocco. Onlaid with red morocco and tooled in gold. Leather joints with red Oasis doublures tooled in gold. Japanese endpapers. Rough-gilt edges. Protective drop-back box in red morocco and cloth. 1969.
Plate 30

Biography

As an amateur Desmond Yardley studied bookbinding at the Central School of Arts and Crafts, London. He made an earlier retirement than normal from his professional career as a bank clerk in order to devote more time to the practice of the craft.

With a frequent preference for making patterns involving the repetition and contrast of simple gold and blind-tooled units, Yardley's work exhibits a dignity and an integrity in its production reflecting the influence of his teachers, George Frewin and William Matthews.

Collections

The British Museum, the Victoria and Albert Museum, the Royal Library at The Hague, Liverpool Public Libraries, the Geographical Institute at Edinburgh, the Reckitt and Colman Collection, and in the U.S.A. at Westminster College, Fulton, Missouri.

Address

Applethwaite, Minstead, Lyndhurst, Hampshire, SO4 7FR.

Bookbinding

52   Ecclesiasticus
Initial letters hand-painted by Graily Hewitt, Ida D. Henstock, and Helen E. Hinckley. Printed by C. H. St. John Hornby at the Ashendene Press, London, 1932. Limited to an edition of 328. Size $11\frac{5}{8} \times 7\frac{7}{8}$ in., 295×200 mm.
Bound in black Oasis morocco with joints and doublures of the same colour and leather. Both covers and doublures lettered over-all in platinum. Head and tail trimmed. 1970.
Plate 31

Tony Appleton Esq.
45

Lt.-Col. P. L. Bradfer-Lawrence
34 49

Mrs. P. L. Bradfer-Lawrence
15

Leon Drucker Esq.
4

Anthony Fair Esq.
5 6 7 13 21 23 28 29 30 31 32 33 35 36 40 41 48

Colin Franklin Esq.
20

Sir John Galvin
38 39 44

The Countess of Iveagh
1 46 47

Mrs. Maggy Magerstadt Rosner
24

Messrs. Henry Sotheran Ltd.
37

The Lord Wardington
2

Photographic Credits

R. B. Fleming & Co., Ltd., London
17 18 24 26 28 30

Norman Jones, London
1 2 3 4 5 6 7 8 9 10 11 12 13 14 15 16 19 21 22 23 25 27 29 31

Endric Lerch, Ascona
20

Designer Bookbinders is greatly indebted to all those who have made this Exhibition possible, and particularly to Mr. Anthony Fair and Lt.-Col. P. L. Bradfer-Lawrence for their special help, advice, and encouragement; to the Cultural Relations Department of the Foreign and Commonwealth Office and the Crafts Council of Great Britain Ltd., for the provision of grants towards the cost of transporting the exhibits to and from America; to Dr. Charles Ryskamp for his Preface to the catalogue and to Mr. John Harthan for contributing the catalogue Introduction; to Mr. Vivian Ridler, Printer to the University of Oxford, for his supervision of the catalogue printing; and to Messrs. George M. Whiley Ltd., for the gift of blocks and foil and for blocking the catalogue covers.

For so kindly offering the hospitality of their display facilities, thanks are due to the Principals of the four libraries mounting the Exhibition—Dr. Charles Ryskamp, Director, and Mr. Frederick Adams Jnr., Director Emeritus, the Pierpont Morgan Library, New York; Dr. Lawrence W. Towner, Director, the Newberry Library, Chicago; Mr. Robert Vosper, University Librarian, University of California, Los Angeles; and Sir John Pope-Hennessy, Director of the Victoria and Albert Museum, London—and to their staffs.

Finally, Designer Bookbinders must record its very sincere thanks to collectors who have loaned and commissioned bindings for the exhibition. This has entailed for them a separation from their books for over eighteen months, and in expressing gratitude the Society is conscious of the fact that without this most generous support a credible presentation of recent British bookbinding could not have been made.

Members

Ivor Robinson MDE FRSA (*President*)
Edgar Mansfield MDE FRSA (*Past President*)
Elizabeth Greenhill (*Hon. Secretary*)
Sally Lou Smith BA (*Hon. Treasurer*)
Anthony Cains
Jeff Clements
Sydney M. Cockerell FRSA
D. G. Etherington
Deborah Evetts
Edward Gray
Arthur Johnson ATD
Trevor Jones ATC
Bernard Middleton FSA FRSA
Ian Ross
Faith Shannon ARCA ATC
Philip Smith ARCA MSIA MDE
E. P. Womersley
Desmond Yardley

Honorary Members

Eric Burdett Esq. MBE
J. Erle Drax Esq.
Anthony Fair Esq.
Miss Christina Foyle
John Harthan Esq. MA FLA
William Matthews Esq.
Mrs. Bernard Middleton
Howard Nixon Esq. BA FSA
The Lord Wardington

Associate Members

Mrs. Kathleen Abbott
Robert C. Akers Esq.
Duncan Andrews Esq. (U.S.A.)
Tony Appleton Esq.
The Reverend M. J. Balchin MA
Mrs. Morar Ballenden
Paul Banks Esq. (U.S.A.)
Mrs. Hilary Barnett ATD
Mrs. Guy Barton
Dr. D. Bigley
Madame B. Boissett
Fru Ingeborg Börjeson (Sweden)
Lt.-Col. P. L. Bradfer-Lawrence MC BA FSA
Christopher Bramwell Esq. (France)
Justin Brooke Esq.
F. W. Brown Esq.

William Bull Esq.
J. A. Burfield Esq.
Mrs. Hanne Brunn (Denmark)
The Honourable Fiona Campbell
S. J. Copeland Esq.
John Corderoy Esq.
Mrs. Stephanie Delbanco
Leon Drucker Esq.
Miss K. R. Drummond
G. Douglas East Esq. MA
Colin Franklin Esq. MA FSA
Robert Freeman Esq.
Hugh Gibson Esq.
H. Goodwin Esq.
Joseph Gradenwitz Esq.
Dr. W. A. D. Griffiths
M. Harris Esq.
Miss Dorothy Harrop MA FLA
Richard Harsher Esq.
Herr Åke Hässler MDE (Sweden)
A. R. A. Hobson Esq. MA
Miss Betty Jean Hogan
Mrs. Barbara Hornby BA
K. E. Houghton Esq.
The Right Honourable the Earl of Iveagh
The Countess of Iveagh
Cedric Nevil Jackson Esq.
William Karatz Esq. (U.S.A.)
Mrs. Ursula Katzenstein (Brazil)
Arthur Last Esq.
Mrs. Denise Lubett
Lef Lubett Esq. ARSM MIMM
Jonathan Macy Esq. (U.S.A.)
Brian D. Maggs Esq.
Richard Minsky Esq. (U.S.A.)
Mrs. David Parkes
Mrs. B. B. Parry
Mrs. Stella Patri (U.S.A.)
Herr Hugo Peller MDE (Switzerland)
Sidney Pizen Esq.
John Plummer Esq.
Harold G. Richardson Esq.
Miss G. Ridgway
Brian Robinson Esq.
Mrs. Magerstadt Rosner (U.S.A.)
Christopher Russell Esq.
David Russell Esq.
Miss Alison Shaw MA
Fred H. Shihader Esq. BA (U.S.A.)
L. G. Simpson Esq.
Ivor Stone Esq.
Arnold Strange Esq.

Miss Rosemary Stubbing
Mrs Brian Tosh
Miss Ann Tout ATD
Peter Waters Esq. ARCA
Mrs. Nicola C. Weiss (U.S.A.)
Herr Carl-G Wiberg MA Knight of the Vasa Order (Sweden)
Mrs. Kathleen Wick (U.S.A.)
Alan Winstanley Esq.

Ivor Robinson   *Chairman*
Elizabeth Greenhill   *Secretary*
Sally Lou Smith   *Treasurer/Selection*
Lt.-Col. P. L. Bradfer-Lawrence
Arthur Johnson
Mrs. Denise Lubett
Bernard Middleton   *Selection/Catalogue*
Faith Shannon
Philip Smith   *Selection/Catalogue/Catalogue Design*
E. P. Womersley

Some of the exhibits are for sale. Details regarding these are
available at the place of exhibition or by application to Miss
Elizabeth Greenhill, Hon. Secretary, Designer Bookbinders,
12 Cornwall Mansions, 33 Kensington Court, London W8 5BG,
Telephone 01-937 2943

1   Anthony Cains (1)
Size 12½ × 10 in., 312 × 255 mm.

2   Anthony Cains (2)
Size 16 × 12½ in., 405 × 317 mm.

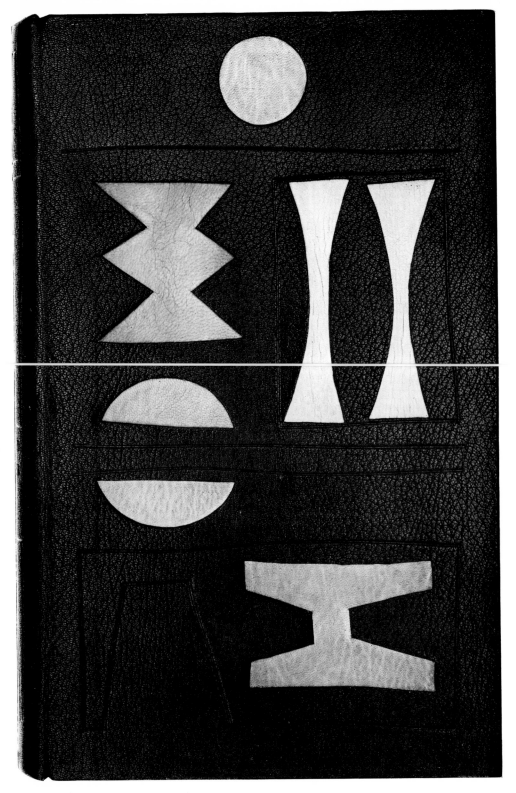

3 **Jeff Clements** (4)
Size $13\frac{3}{4} \times 8\frac{1}{4}$ in., 350×210 mm.

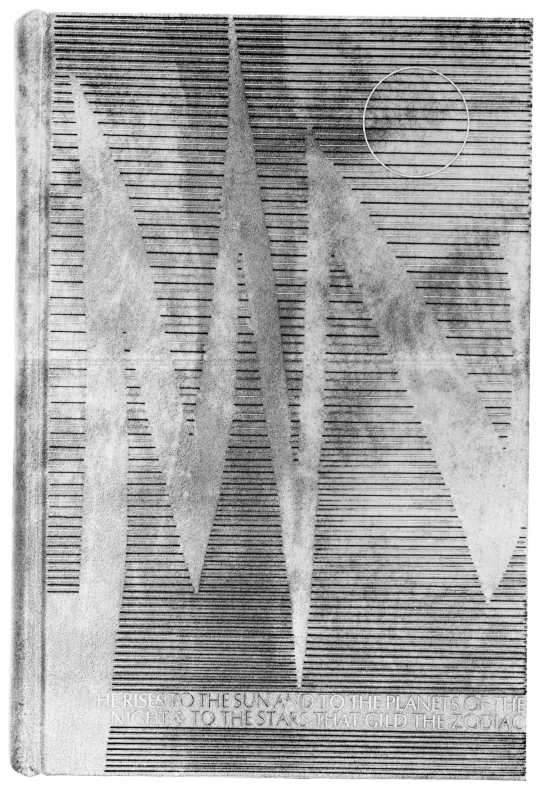

HE RISES TO THE SUN AND TO THE PLANETS OF THE
NIGHT & TO THE STARS THAT GILD THE ZODIAC

4   Sydney M. Cockerell (6)
Size 10¾×7⅝ in., 273×195 mm.

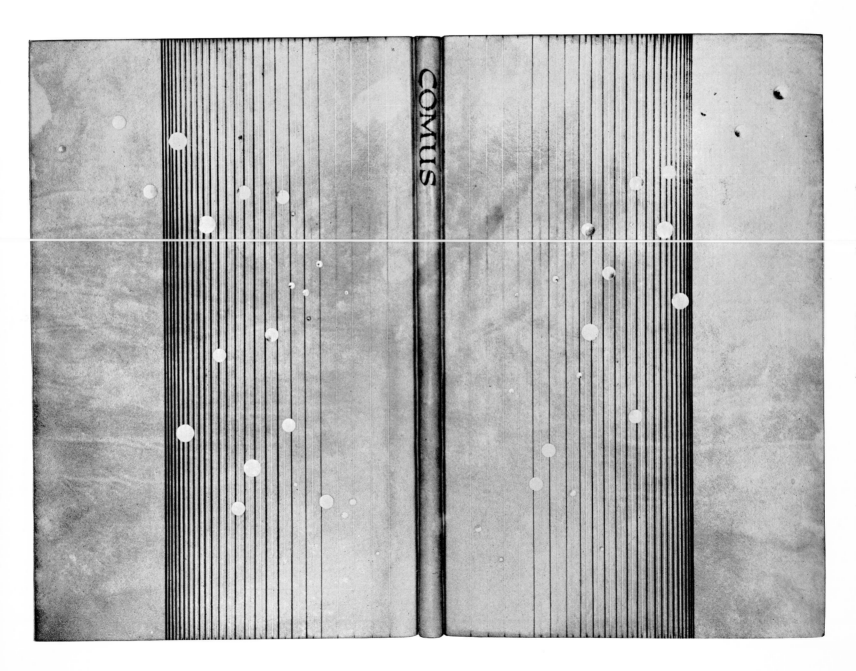

5   Sydney M. Cockerell (7)
Size 15⅛×10⅛ in., 384×257 mm.

6   Deborah Evetts (10)
Size $5\frac{1}{2} \times 4\frac{1}{4}$ in., 140×108 mm.

7   Deborah Evetts (11)
Size 6½ × 4⅝ in., 165 × 118 mm.

8 **Elizabeth Greenhill (13)**
Size 12¼ × 9 in., 311 × 229 mm.

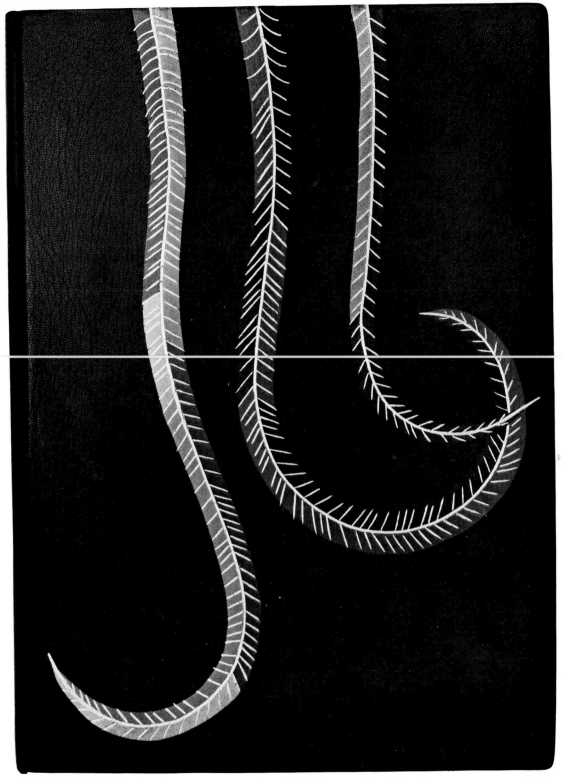

9 Elizabeth Greenhill (15)
Size 12 × 9 in., 305 × 229 mm.

10   Arthur Johnson (18)
Size 15⅛ × 11⅞ in., 385 × 303 mm.

MALLEUS
MALEFICARUM

11   Trevor Jones (19)
Size $11\frac{3}{4} \times 6\frac{7}{8}$ in., 299×170 mm.

THE ECLOGUES OF VERGIL

12   Edgar Mansfield (20)
Size 13½ × 10¼ in., 343 × 260 mm.

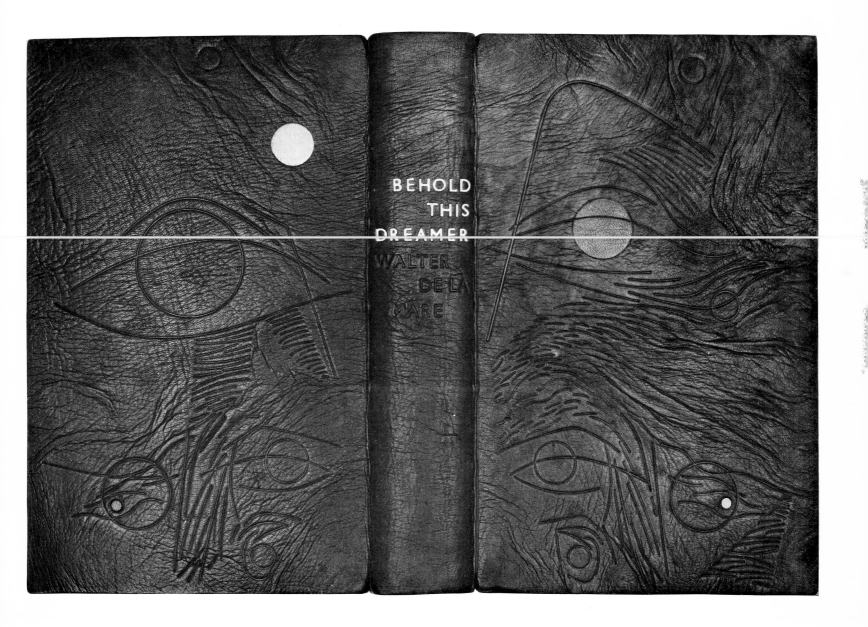

Text on spine: BEHOLD THIS DREAMER / WALTER DE LA MARE

13   Edgar Mansfield (21)
Size 9⅛ × 6⅛ in., 232 × 155 mm.

14   Edgar Mansfield (23)
Size 17 × 13½ in., 432 × 343 mm.

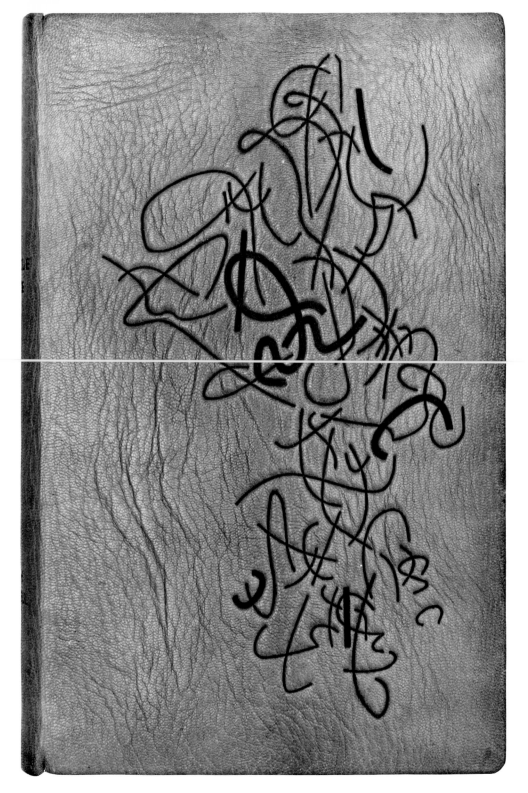

15   Edgar Mansfield (24)
Size 8⅞ × 5⅞ in., 226 × 150 mm.

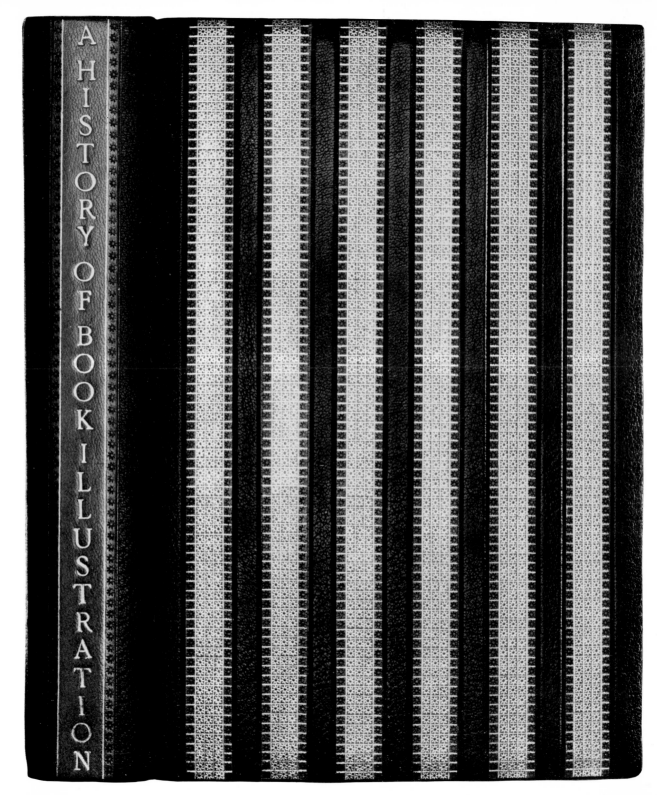

16   Bernard Middleton (25)
Size 10¾×7½ in., 273×190 mm.

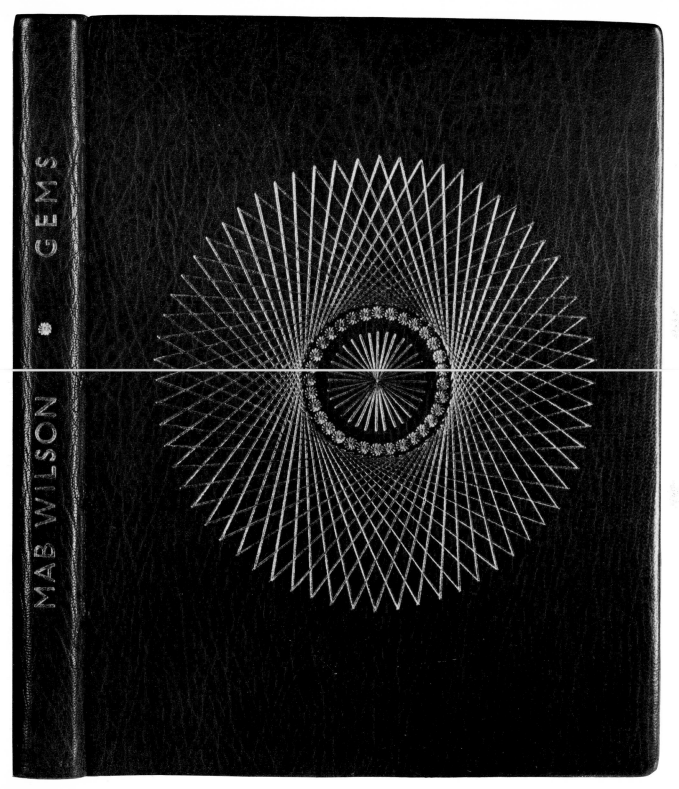

17 **Bernard Middleton (27)**
Size 9½×7⅝ in., 241×194 mm.

18   Ivor Robinson (29)
Size $13\frac{3}{8} \times 10\frac{1}{4}$ in., 340×260 mm.

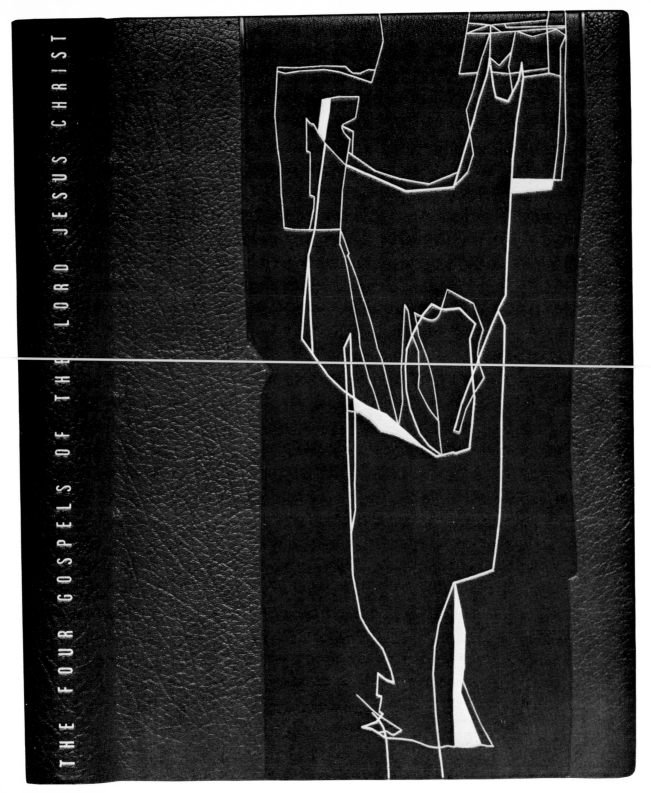

19   Ivor Robinson (32)
Size 13¼ × 9 in., 335 × 230 mm.

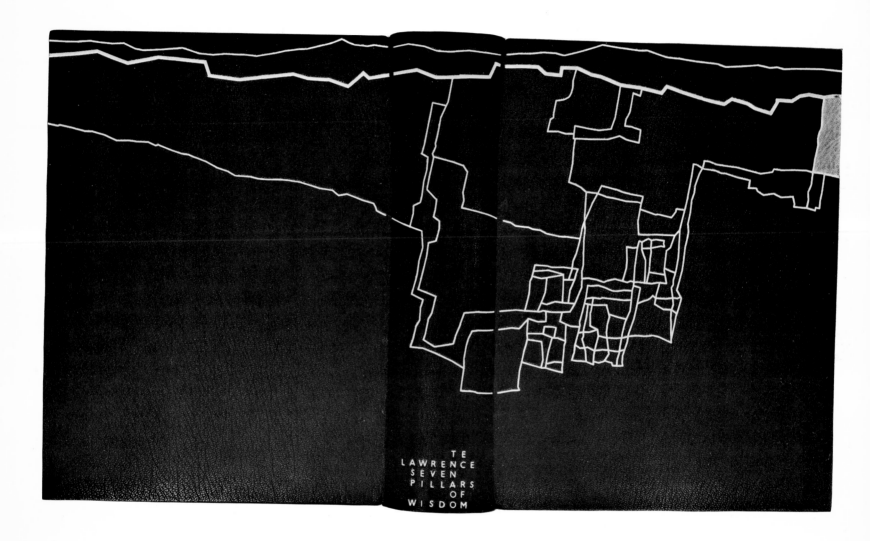

TE
LAWRENCE
SEVEN
PILLARS
OF
WISDOM

20   Ivor Robinson (34)
Size 10⅛×7⅜ in., 255×190 mm.

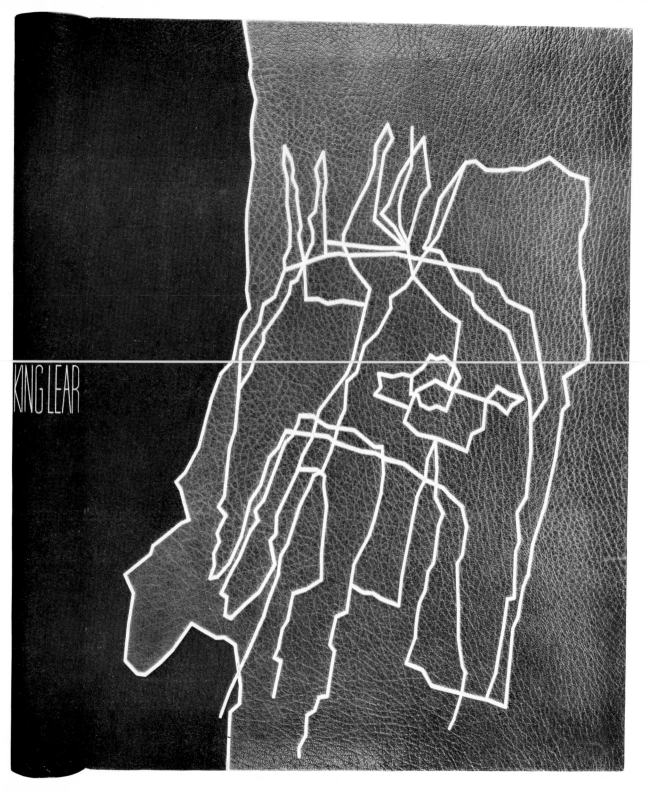

21   Ivor Robinson (35)
Size 18⅜ × 14 in., 465 × 355 mm.

22 **Faith Shannon (37)**
Size 10⅛ × 7¼ in., 258 × 184 mm.

23   Philip Smith (38)
Size 13¾×10¼ in., 345×260 mm.

24 **Philip Smith (40)**
Size 15 × 11½ in , 375 × 290 mm.

25   Philip Smith (41)
Size $18 \times 14\frac{1}{4}$ in., 457×360 mm.

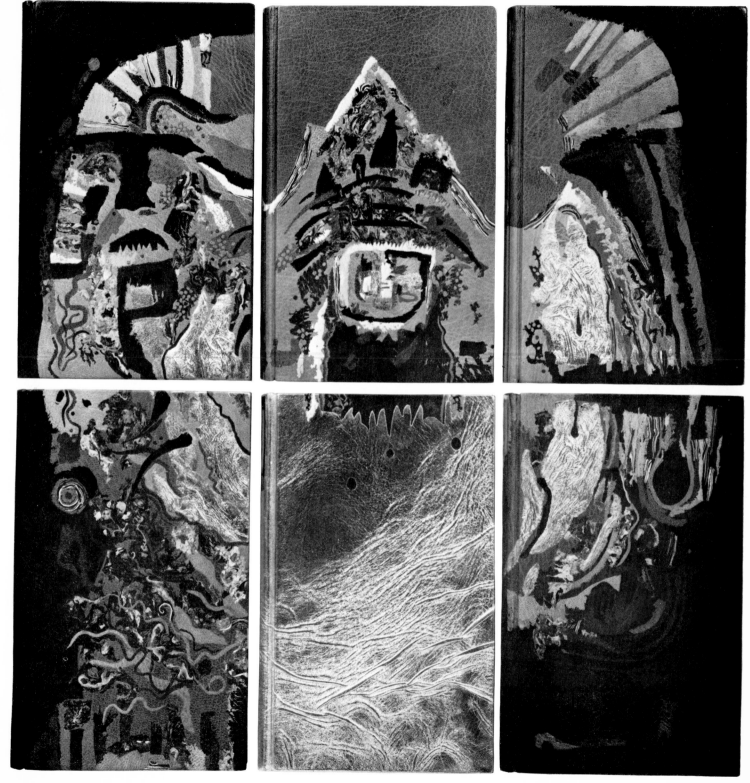

26   Philip Smith (42)
Each book size $9\frac{1}{8} \times 5\frac{7}{8}$ in., 270×150 mm.

27 **Philip Smith (44)**
Size 6⅜ × 4 in., 160 × 100 mm.

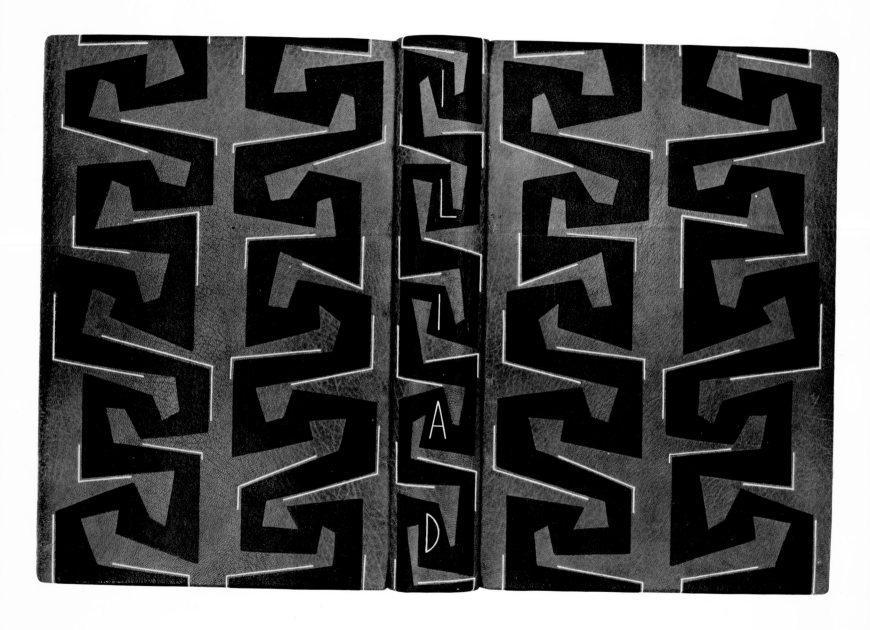

28   Sally Lou Smith (48)
Size 11⅛×7⅝ in., 285×195 mm.

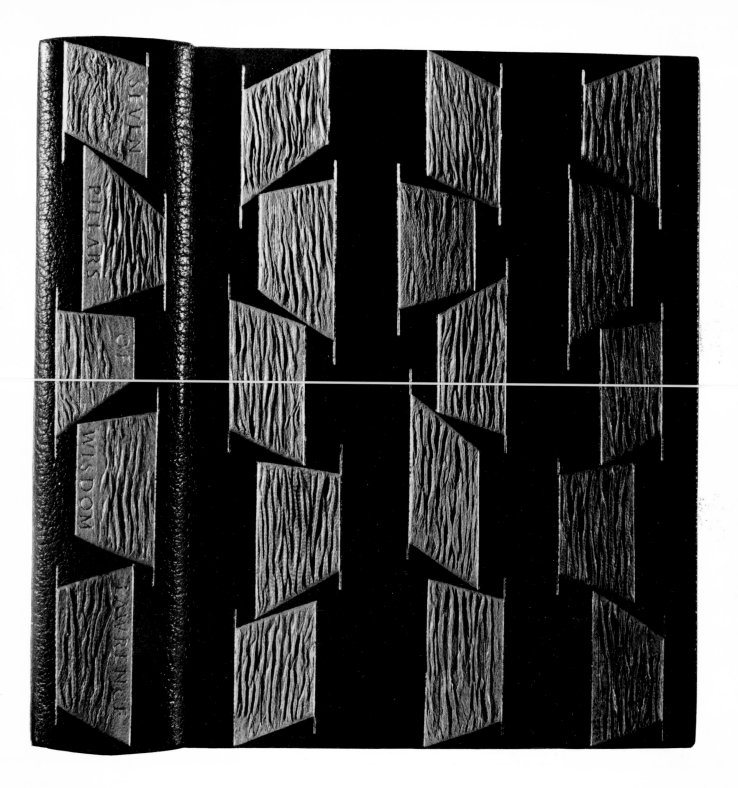

29   Sally Lou Smith **(49)**
Size 10 × 7¾ in., 250 × 198 mm.

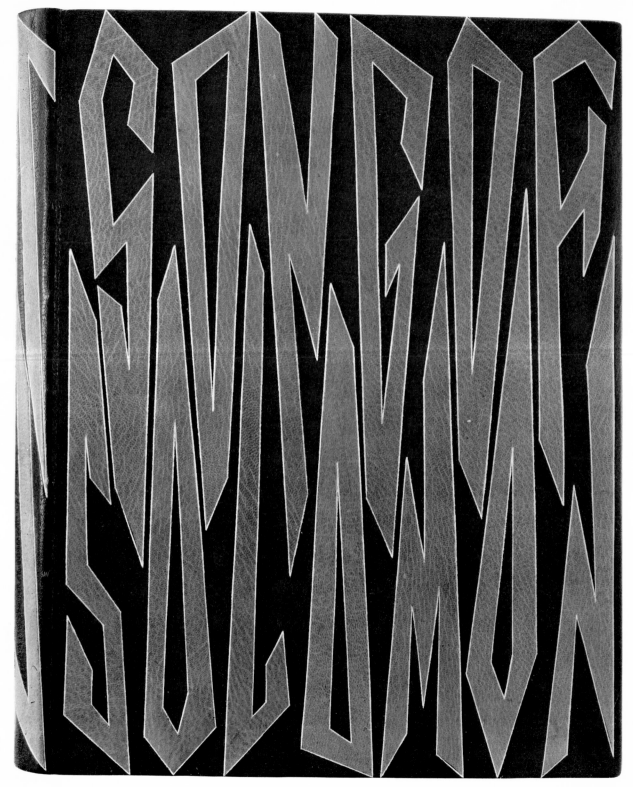

30   Sally Lou Smith (51)
Size 15×12¼ in., 383×312 mm.

HIS MIND TO FINISH HIS WORK
AND WATCHETH TO POLISH IT
PERFECTLY.
SO IS THE POTTER SITTING
AT HIS WORK & TURNING THE
WHEEL ABOUT WITH HIS FEET,
WHO IS ALWAY ANXIOUSLY SET
AT HIS WORK AND MAKETH ALL
HIS WORK BY NUMBER.
HE FASHIONETH THE CLAY WITH
HIS ARM & BOWETH DOWN HIS
STRENGTH BEFORE HIS FEET.
HE APPLIETH HIMSELF TO FIN-
ISH THE GLAZING, AND HE IS
DILIGENT TO MAKE CLEAN
THE FURNACE.
ALL THESE TRUST TO THEIR
HANDS, AND EACH BECOMETH

ECCLESIASTICUS

WISE IN HIS OWN WORK.
WITHOUT THESE CANNOT A CITY
BE INHABITED, AND WHEREVER
THEY DWELL THEY HUNGER NOT.
THEY SHALL NOT BE SOUGHT
FOR IN PUBLICK COUNSEL NOR
SIT HIGH IN THE CONGREGAT
ION: THEY SHALL NOT SIT ON
THE JUDGES SEAT NOR UNDER-
STAND THE SENTENCE OF JUDG-
MENT: THEY CANNOT DECLARE
JUSTICE AND JUDGMENT, AND
THEY SHALL NOT BE FOUND
WHERE PARABLES ARE SPOKEN.
BUT THEY WILL MAINTAIN
THE FABRIC OF THE WORLD,
AND IN THE HANDYWORK OF
THEIR CRAFT IS THEIR PRAYER.

ASHEN
-DENE
PRESS
1932

31 **Desmond Yardley (52)**
Size 11⅝ × 7⅞ in., 295 × 200 mm.